Meet Us at the
National Parks

Including National Parks, Monuments, Historical Sites, and More

Written by Andrew F. Johnson

Illustrated by Jennifer Johnson Haywood

Kids can become official Junior Rangers! There are hundreds of different Junior Ranger programs available throughout the United States. Ask at any National Park Service (NPS) visitor center to see if a local program is offered. Also, you may look online to see a current listing of participating parks.

Complete the fun activities, games and puzzles in the Junior Ranger packet. Then you may stop by a visitor center to receive your Junior Ranger badge, patch, or pin.

For those who cannot visit a park, try the online program called WebRanger. This allows kids to become Junior Rangers over the Internet.

In memory of Ethan T. Johnson, an advocate of science, the arts, outdoor exploration, and fun.

Published by HAYWOOD STUDIOS INC.
Hastings, Michigan 49058 U.S.A.
Jr. RangerLand™ is a registered trademark of Haywood Studios Inc.

Printed in the United States of America

Second Printing, First Edition 2011

Publisher's Cataloging-in-Publication data

Johnson, Andrew F., 1949 -
    Meet us at the national parks / Andrew F. Johnson ; illustrated by Jennifer Johnson Haywood.
    p. cm.
    ISBN 978-0-615-38995-0
    Summary : An exploration of the sights, landscape, animals, and landmarks of the U.S. national parks.

1. National parks and reserves --United States --Juvenile literature. 2. Outdoor recreation --United States --Juvenile literature. 3. United States -- Description and travel --Juvenile literature. I. Haywood, Jennifer Johnson. II. Title.

E160 .J63 2011
333.78/3/0973 --dc22   2010942470

Haywood Studios Inc. and Jr. RangerLand™ are not associated with the National Park Service.
We wish to thank Leslie, Matt, and Melina for their expertise in editing this book.
For more information about Jr. Rangerland products please visit our website: www.jr-rangerland.com

Sophie, Anna, Kate, and Mark learn from friends in every park.
They have fun along the way as they cross the USA.

Looking out from Ruby Beach, Aidan sees an orca breach.

Ethan takes his hiking gear
when he goes to Mount Rainier.

Ida, Aggie, Drew, and Gayle
spot a pika from the trail.

Eli, Dan, and brother Sam
love to ride the Zion Tram.

Hoodoos high and hoodoos deep,
Kenzie sees them in her sleep.

Pat spies arches way up high, looking like they touch the sky.

Pools and geysers, wolves, and bear: Matt's exploring everywhere.

Abby doesn't have a doubt; she will catch a rainbow trout.

Jena sees, beyond the plain,
land that's formed by wind and rain.

George and Thomas, Abe and Ted,
Mr. Borglum carved each head.

Junior Rangers want to know all about the lava flow.

Up above the rough terrain, Sara flies with Mary Jane.

From Hannah's boat, she can see glacier ice that's breaking free.

Ranger Mel says please don't stray. Feeding bears is **NOT** okay.

Michael likes the boat tour best. There he spots an osprey nest.

Paul Revere rode late at night once he saw the church's light.

Erica and friends from school
see reflections in the pool.

Jamie finds, to his delight,
ruins in the Old Town site.

Soldiers led by General George
wintered here at Valley Forge.

Frank and Amy, Beth and Paul
take some pictures of the Hall.

High above is Anne-Marie,
standing by Miss Liberty.

Ranger Rita likes to teach
all the children at the beach.

Some are common. Some are rare. Dee finds flowers everywhere.

Salamanders red and black like to hide from Jay and Jack.

Dena spots some wolves and moose
running through a field of spruce.

Up the steps Ray likes to march
on his way to see the Arch.

Lucia has a special wish:
go and swim with schools of fish.

Jola's careful where she stomps
due to 'gators in the swamps.

Cho is looking very small
because the redwoods are so tall.

Kimana thinks it's lots of fun
counting lizards in the sun.

Grayson, Kit, and Marisol stand beside the waterfall.

Lynn and Emma think it's great in the parks at Golden Gate.

Miska sees the bighorns hop all across the mountaintop.

David's feeling really brave.
It's so dark inside the cave.

Rosh and Dillon find a quail
as they walk Comanche Trail.

Juan and Mansi, Kim and Alice
take a tour of Cliff Palace.

When out hiking, Flo and Glenn
listen to the cactus wren.

Izzy loves to camp at night and waken by the Canyon's light.

When out traveling near and far, on a train or in a car,
exploring parks is so much fun; kids can visit every one.